Playing With Words:
Sound Effect Poe

Selected by Bri

Contents

Longman

Edinburgh Gate
Harlow, Essex

Day in the Life of Me

Day dawn,
Stretch yawn,
Rise and shine
Breakfast time.
Mum fuss,
School bus,
Run around
Playground.
Read, write,
Tease and fight.
Queue for lunch,
Monster munch.
No surprise,
Time flies,
Half three,
Time for tea.
In the park
Until dark.
Quick nosh,
Then wash,
Hamster fed,
Time for bed.
Rain storm,
Bed warm,
Count sheep,
Deep sleep.

Andrew Fusek Peters

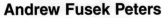

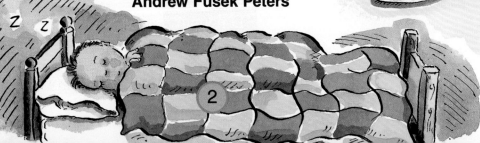

Riddle

I can whistle
a tune.
I can sing.
I can croon.

I'm a friend
to the trees.
I'm a buzz
for the bees.

On a night
dark and deep
I will keep
you from sleep

When I mutter
and roar
and moan
round your door.

I'm as wild
as a lion
or mild
as a lamb ...

Do you know
who I am?

Ann Bonner

Jellyfish

Jellyfish,
jellyfish,
floats along and slaps you on the belly
fish.

Just when you thought you'd go for a swim,
just when you thought it was safe to go in.

Jellyfish,
jellyfish,
saw one in a programme on the telly
fish.

Thinking about it kept me awake,
I just don't think that I can take

jellyfish,
jellyfish,
trod on one at Margate with Aunt Nelly
fish.

If you see one in the sea then give me a shout,
catch it in a bucket but keep your fingers out.

Jellyfish,
jellyfish,
odd and funny-looking umbrelly
fish,
slimy old seaside smelly
fish,

jellyfish,
jellyfish,
jellyfish,
jellyfish.

Brian Moses

4

Sounds of Summer

The sea says, "Hush!"
On a sunny day,
The waves say, "Splash!"
When the dolphins play.

The stones say, "Clunk!"
On their sandy bed,
And the gulls say, "Kraaark!"
As they steal my bread.

Clare Bevan

Sounds Familiar

Thump!
That's my brother jumping out of bed.
Frrrrrp!
That's the blind rolling up.
Clunk!
That's the door handle turning.
SHSHshshsh …
That's the toilet flushing.
Thud, thud, thud, thud, thud …
That's my brother running downstairs.

Same old brother.
Same old sounds every morning.
Sounds of home.
Sounds of family.

Sounds great!

Penny Kent

Lunch Button

Plip, plop, drip, drop,
gulp, gulp, CRUNCH!
Don't worry,
It's only my **Magic Munch Machine**
at work on my magic lunch!

Drip, drop, plip, plop,
glug, gulp, SMACK!
Don't worry,
it's only my **Magic Munch Machine**
at work on my magic snack!

Judith Nicholls

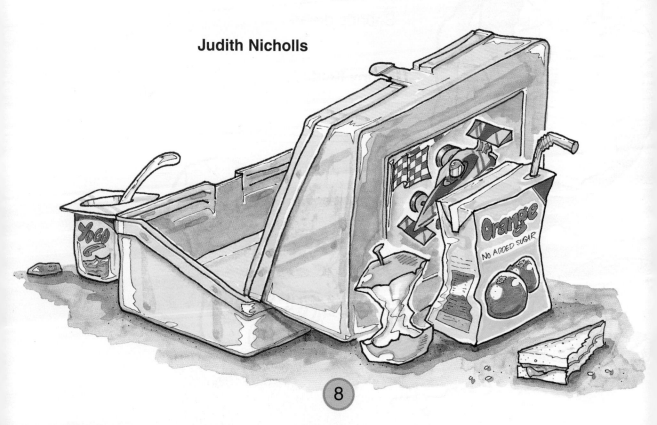

Riddle

My **1st** is in wishing and also in hope,

My **2nd's** in towel and also in soap,

My **3rd** is in sleep and also in lie,

My **4th** is in fruit and also in pie,

My **5th** is in day and also in dark,

My **6th** is in boat and also in ark,

My **7th's** in yes and also in nay,

My **whole** is a time to relax and play.

Celia Warren

Riddle

I run ahead, and follow you,
Whether you're slow or fast,
I stay with you up to your gate,
But then go straight on past!

Liz Brownlee

Riddle

My first is in fish but not in chip.

My second in teeth but not in lip.

My third's in potato but not in plum.

My fourth's in mouth and also in thumb.

My fifth is in pear but not in cherry.

My sixth is in bacon but not in berry.

My last is in chocolate but not in crumble.

Sometimes when I'm empty you'll hear me rumble.

John Foster

The Yaffling Yahoo

(A Do-It-Yourself Space Beast)

The Yaffling Yahoo
is made of blue glue,
but when she feels mean
she turns a bright ...

She shrinks herself small
when dry rain starts to fall.
She's an ugly disgrace
with those splumps on her ...

She enjoys a long drink
from a tank of thick ink,
then will sprint down the street
on her twelve pairs of ....

When her back gets an itch
her glue nose starts to twitch.
She is skyscraper tall
yet as round as a ...

The Yaffling Yahoo
just hasn't a clue.
She continues to chase
through the dark depths of ...

Wes Magee

14

The Aquarium

The aquarium
was disappointing:

The dogfish
didn't bark,
the jellyfish
didn't wobble.

The sea mouse
didn't squeak,
the starfish
didn't shine.

The hermit crabs
were crabby,
the clams
clammed up,
and the plaice
stayed in one place.

But when the swordfish
attacked us,
and the sharks invited us
to be their lunch …

we rode away fast …
on a seahorse!

Brian Moses

Out in the Desert

Out in the desert lies the sphinx
It never eats and it never drinx
Its body quite solid without any chinx
And when the sky's all purples and pinx
(As if it was painted with coloured inx)
And the sun it ever so swiftly sinx
Behind the hills in a couple of twinx
You may hear (if you're lucky) a bell that clinx
And also tolls and also tinx
And they say at the very same sound the sphinx
It sometimes smiles and it sometimes winx:

But nobody knows just what it thinx.

Charles Causley

16

Wordspinning

Spin pins into nips.
Snap pans into naps.
Mix spit into tips.
Turn parts into traps.

Switch post on to stop.
Whisk dear into dare.
Carve hops into shop.
Rip rate into tear.

Twist tame into mate.
Make mean into name.
Juggle taste into state
In the wordspinning game.

John Foster

Can You?

Can you cross the bridge in your nose
and run between the gap in your teeth
to mend the roof in your mouth
with the nails in your toes?
No!
Well why not climb the palm in your hand
and watch out for the swallow in your throat.
Or,
just get up early one morning instead
and catch the hares asleep on your head!

Ian Souter

Summer Storm

Hailstones
beat down the beans
battered the hanging baskets
bounced on the patio chairs.

Wind
whipped through the roses
whirled petals high
whammed against fences.

Rain
lashed at the greenhouse
landed in the fish pond
laid the tall lupins low.

'Just to let you know,'
said the weather,
'That I'm still
out and about.'

Patricia Leighton

Catch Words

Throw me a WORD – we'll play CATCH
   Throw me ITCH – I'll throw you …?
Throw me RED – I'll throw you HOT
   Throw me TEA – I'll throw you …?

   Throw me DUST – I'll throw you BIN
Throw me BANANA – I'll throw you …?
   Throw me BANGERS – I'll throw you MASH
And if you drop a word or two
   I'll throw you … SMASH!

Mandy Coe

22

RHYME-OSAUR

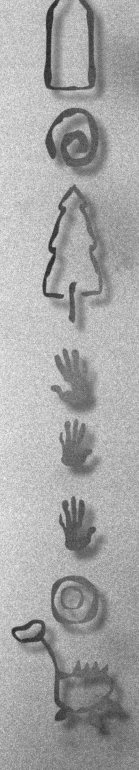

Out of a deep, dark mine-osaur
at roughly half past nine-osaur,
there came a sleepy stegosaur
into the warm sunshine-osaur.
He warmed his chilly spine-osaur
which made him feel divine-osaur.

He nibbled on a pine-osaur
and drank a glass of wine-osaur.
But then he saw a sign-osaur
which made him yelp and whine-osaur.

It forecast his decline-osaur –
his time had come to die-nosaur!

John Rice

Squid Soup

A sea snake sipped soup with a seagull.
"When you sip," squawked the seagull, "you slurp.
Stop slurping, you slithering sea snake."
The sea snake said "Sssssssss" and went "Shshshshlurp!"
So the gull slyly swallowed the sea snake.
"Hissssss," said the snake as she slid,
slithering, into the seagull
who then swallowed the soup, which was squid.

Marian Swinger

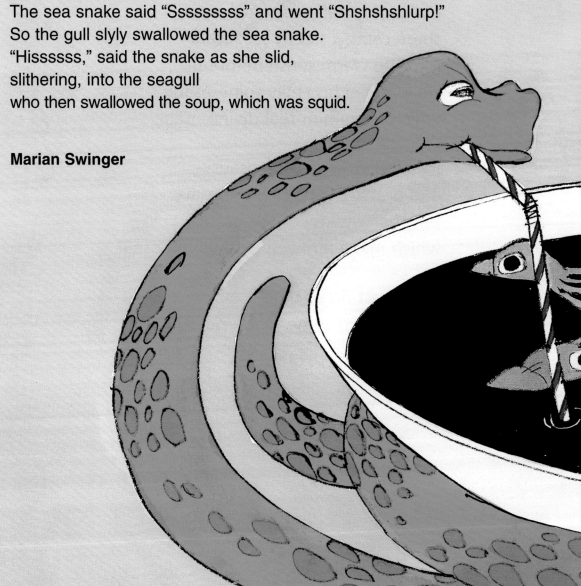

Playing with Words

I've been playing with words.

I threw 'CATCH' into the air –

And dropped it.

I've kicked the 'LL' out of 'BALL'

(Which has left me with 'BA').

I've wiped the floor with 'MOP'

And I've given 'STOMACH' a good prod.

I've sat on 'CUSHION'

 And 'MARBLE' has just rolled under the sofa.

Mum says that 'LOUNGE' isn't for lazing

And that I've made it look a right 'MESS'

So I've got to collect up

All the words again

And put them away – *tidily* –

In my Dictionary.

Before Dad gets home.

By Trevor Harvey

Kitchen Concert

The concert is beginning
   and the kitchen
      tunes up, ready
        to face the day.

The fridge purrs,
   the freezer growls
      the mixer whirrs,
        and the toaster pops.

The kettle sings,
   the sink gurgles,
      the pan bubbles,
        and the mincer chops.

The microwave pings,
   the timer chirps,
      the percolator chuckles,
        and the clock ticks.

The hot tap gushes,
   the washer hums,
      the dryer whirls,
        and the off-switch clicks.

The concert is over
   but the kitchen
      murmurs to itself
        throughout the night.

Moira Andrew

Sounds

Miss asked if we had any favourite sounds,
and could we quickly write them down.
Tim said the screeeeam of a mean guitar
or a saxophone or a fast sports car.
Shakira said cats when they purrrrr on your lap,
and Karen, the **CRASH** of a thunderclap.
Paul asked what word he could possibly write
for the sound of a rocket on Guy Fawkes Night,
or a redwood tree as it fell to the ground,
and Miss said to write it as it sounds.
So Paul wrote Whooooooooooooosh with a dozen "o"s
and **CRACK** with a crack in it, just to show
the kind of noise a tree might make
as it hit the ground and made it **SHAKE**.
Then everyone called, "Hey listen to this!
what do you think? Is this right Miss?
Do balloons go **POP!** or Bust or **BANG** ?
Do church bells **DONG** or Peeeeeal or just **CLANG**?"
Then Miss said it was quite enough
and time to stop all the silly stuff.
What she really likes, as she's often said
is a quiet room, with every head
bent over books, writing things down –
the sound of silence, her favourite sound!

Brian Moses

Cup-Final

T. O'Day

W. E. March   T. O. G. Lory

J. Usty   O. Uwait   N. See

G. O'Dow

A. Day   W. Ewill   N. Infa   H. I. Story

Young   N. Fast   M. O'Reskill   I. T. Sreally

W. Egot

A. L. L. Sewnup   W. E. Rethel   A. D. S. Whollrun

A. Round   W. Embley

W. I. Thecup

Roger McGough

29

Someone Stole The

While I was taking a short cat-nap

someone stole the cat,

I should have spun round like a catherine wheel

when someone stole the cat.

But I was too slow to catch them,

when someone stole the cat.

Now the catamaran can't float,

because someone stole the cat.

And the caterpillar can't crawl,

because someone stole the cat.

And the cataract can't fall,

because someone stole the cat.

It was not me and it was not you

but it is categorically true,

And if you were to ask me

I'd say it was a catastrophe

that someone's stolen the cat.

Brian Patten

Don't Be Such a Fusspot

Don't be such a fusspot,
an always-in-a-rushpot.

Don't be such a weepypot,
a sneak-to-mum-and-be-creepypot.

Don't be such a muddlepot,
a double-dose-of-troublepot.

Don't be such a wigglepot,
a sit-on-your-seat-don't-squigglepot.

Don't be such a muckypot,
a pick-up-slugs-and-be-yuckypot.

Don't be such a sleepypot,
a beneath-the-bedclothes-peepypot.

Don't be such a fiddlepot,
a mess-about-and-meddlepot.

Don't be such a bossypot,
a saucypot, a gigglepot,
don't be such a lazypot,
a nigglepot, a slackpot.

And don't call me a crackpot …
Who do you think you are?

Brian Moses

Answers to riddles